Andrew. K. Kennedy.

KU-427-340

THE
BIG BOOK
OF
MACHINES
IN COLOUR

MARION 8900: American drag-line machine. Weight: 6,000 tons. Power: 18,000 h.p. Throw: 275 ft. Bucket capacity: 200 tons. Used for coal mining.

COLLINS
LONDON AND GLASGOW

ROADMAKING

The construction of a new road provides a good opportunity to see big machines at work. In the early stages it is the earth movers which fill the air with the throbbing of their engines and the clanking of their scoops and blades.

Most fascinating of these is the bulldozer. This is the machine which can flatten mountains, fill valleys and divert rivers. It indeed changes the face of the earth.

Perhaps the reason for this fascination is that most of us have dug a garden using a fork and spade, and are awed by the power which enables these big machines to move in minutes a quantity of earth which would take weeks to move by hand.

TRACKED LOADER: Caterpillar 977K.
Engine: 177 h.p.   Bucket capacity: 4½ tons.

HYDRAULIC EXCAVATOR: Bamford 7C.
Bucket capacity: 1½ tons.   Digging depth: 21 ft.

WHEEL LOADER: Aveling-Barford.
Engine: 185-200 h.p.   Bucket capacity: 4½-5½ tons.

Scraper-loader machines are used for moving earth a relatively long distance. They consist of a strong wheeled frame supporting a massive bowl which can be raised and lowered. In operation, the bowl of the scraper is lowered as it is being towed along, so that earth is scooped up into the bowl.

The Caterpillar 666 wheel tractor scraper has a bowl capacity of 75 tons.

The construction of a road involves a great deal of levelling and surface grading. Bulldozers can be used for some of this work, but special, more versatile grading machines have been developed to do it more efficiently. This is the American Caterpillar 16 grading machine. Powered by a 225 h.p. 6-cylinder diesel engine, the Cat 16 has a 14-ft. blade and weighs 21 tons.

Aveling Austin Super Heavy 500 grading machine. Powered by a
183 h.p. General Motors engine, this machine weighs 15 tons.
The hydraulic cylinders used for raising and lowering the scraper
blade are clearly visible. The blade can be set at any angle to the
direction of movement, and can be swung to the side for shaping
the sides of cuttings. The blade
can also be replaced with a claw
attachment for ripping the surface.

TRENCHER: Winget-Parsons 221.
Engine: 55 h.p. Digging depth: 8 ft. 6 in.
Width of trench: 2-4 ft. Weight: 14 tons.

PIPE LAYER: Caterpillar 594.
Engine: 385 h.p. Lifting capacity: 100 tons.
Weight: 60 tons. Counter-weight: 12 tons.

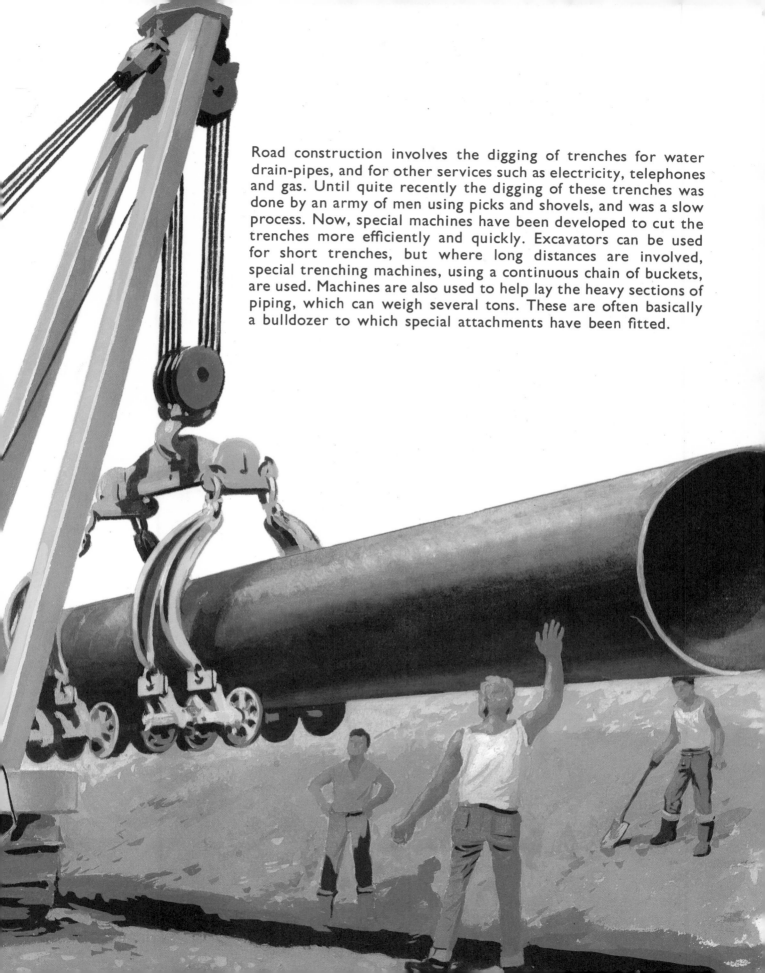

Road construction involves the digging of trenches for water drain-pipes, and for other services such as electricity, telephones and gas. Until quite recently the digging of these trenches was done by an army of men using picks and shovels, and was a slow process. Now, special machines have been developed to cut the trenches more efficiently and quickly. Excavators can be used for short trenches, but where long distances are involved, special trenching machines, using a continuous chain of buckets, are used. Machines are also used to help lay the heavy sections of piping, which can weigh several tons. These are often basically a bulldozer to which special attachments have been fitted.

Special machines have been designed for laying the concrete foundation and wearing surface. The concrete used in road making is called *dry lean,* and consists of only about one part of cement to twenty parts of sand and stone.

The *dry lean* is laid flat and smoothly without any interruption, the hopper on some of the latest laying machines being capable of being recharged on the move by side-tipper trucks. The same machine can also spread the top surface of bitumen or asphalt.

PAVER FINISHER: Blaw Knox PF-90.
Engine: 65 h.p.   Capacity: 8-16 ft. wide by up to 12 in. deep.
Working speed: 42 ft. per minute.   Hopper capacity: 10 tons.

PNEUMATIC TYRED COMPACTER: Aveling-Barford PTR 30.
Engine: 78 h.p. Weight: 15 tons. Working speed: 15 m.p.h.

Machine power at its peak is evident in the making of a motorway. Ordinary road construction and repairs often does not allow full advantage to be taken of the machines available. On motorways, however, planned in relatively long stretches and often laid out through open country, full scope can be given to the roadmaking machines.

Scrapers and bulldozers are used by the dozen and work in teams. Huge trains are used to lay the concrete foundation. Shown below is an American-designed machine, known as a Slipform Paver, built in Belgium for use in Europe. This can lay up to two miles in a day.

McGregor

One of the main advantages of a motorway is that the flow of vehicles is not hindered by crossing traffic, as happens at normal crossroads. This means that a large number of bridges either to carry the motorway over other roads, or bridges to carry other roads over the motorway need to be constructed. Some bridges are cast in position, but many are made up from pre-cast members lifted into position by mobile cranes.

A Coles Centurion mobile crane lifting a 120-ton concrete beam into position during the construction of the M1 extension to Leeds. This was one of the heaviest pre-cast beams ever made for a British motorway bridge.

BUILDING

A wide variety of machines are used in the construction of buildings. Their activity interests most people, so much so that contractors leave 'windows' in the surrounding hoarding so that passers-by can watch the work in progress.

Two machines found on almost any building site are the concrete mixer and crane. The illustration shows a mobile concrete mixer made by Stothert and Pitt, which can mix over 14 tons of concrete at a time. To the right is a tower crane also made by Stothert and Pitt. This can handle a 2½-ton load with a 40-ft. jib and 1 ton with a 100-ft. jib.

Typical of the excavators for use on building sites are:—

1. FRENCH POCLAIN GC 120. 110 h.p.

2. HY-MAC 1080. 165 h.p.

3. MUSTANG 90, with digging grab. 94 h.p.

Cranes are among the most interesting of all machines. Few people can resist the temptation to stop and gaze when they pass one about to lift something, whether it be a jib-crane tending a broken-down motor car, or a tower crane on a building site.
Special cranes have been developed for almost every task involving lifting.

FAIRY SAPPHIRE: Small mobile crane.
Capacity: 6 tons, to a height of 35 ft.

NEAL NU 1620: Medium crane.
Capacity: $15\frac{1}{2}$ tons.

GROVE: Telescopic-jib crane. Capacity: 45 tons

Among the biggest are the giant walking drag-line cranes used for mining operations where the ore lies near the surface. Among the most unusual are the part bulldozer, part crane vehicles used to move crashed aircraft from runways. Mobile cranes are, of course, used for a wide variety of jobs.

Shown below are three Centurion cranes being used together to erect a giant steel chimney in South Wales. The use of cranes together in this manner requires great skill on the part of the crane operators who have to harmonize their movements.

FARMING

Nowhere has the introduction of machines been of greater benefit than in farming. Indeed, without their valuable help, it would be impossible for the world to feed its teeming millions. Farmers use machines to prepare the soil for the crop, to help maintain its fertility, to help plant the crop and then, with the aid of machines such as the Ransomes Cavalier combine harvester shown above, to harvest the crop.

CLAAS SENATOR.
German combine harvester.
Engine: 145 h.p.
Output of grain: 10 tons per hour.
Capacity of grain tank: 88 bushels.

NEW HOLLAND CLAYSON M140.
American combine harvester.
Engine: 128 h.p.
Output of grain: 12 tons per hour.
Capacity of grain tank: 75 bushels.

MASSEY-FERGUSON 515.
British combine harvester.
Engine: 106 h.p.
Output of grain: 9 tons per hour.
Capacity of grain tank: 70 bushels.

LELY VICTORY.
British combine harvester.
Engine: 135 h.p.
Output of grain: 17 tons per hour.
Capacity of grain tank: 85 bushels.
This machine, made by Fisher-Humphries, has one of the highest outputs of any combine harvester.

The reel of the Clayson combine harvester, on the left, is in the towed position for moving to the field. All combine harvesters have this arrangement, except the Lely, on which the reel is jointed and folds up for towing.

BM VOLVO S950.
Swedish combine harvester.
Engine: 117 h.p.
Output of grain: 10 tons per hour.
Capacity of grain tank: 66 bushels.

MASSEY-FERGUSON 1100: 105 h.p. British.

JOHN DEERE 5020: 143 h.p. American.

DAVID BROWN 1200: 67 h.p. British.

FORD 5,000: 75 h.p. British.

The most important and widely used of all farm machines is the tractor. This, of course, has replaced the horse of bygone days. With its large wheels, giving it great pulling power and enabling it to cross muddy ground, tractors are used for a wide variety of jobs. Tractors are employed basically to pull implements, such as ploughs, and to provide power for attachments, such as cutters for hedge-trimming, light cranes and fork lifts.

Tractor pulling a five-furrow plough. Ploughs digging up to 8 furrows are used on big farms.

BMC NUFFIELD 4/65: 65 h.p. British.

COUNTY 1124: 113 h.p. British.

DUTRA D4K-B: 100 h.p. Hungarian.

MATBRO MASTIFF: 128 h.p. British.

SAME LEONE 70: 67 h.p. Italian.

TRANSPORT

One of the newest machines to be developed is the hovercraft, or rather, the air cushion vehicle. As the name implies, these strange craft, part aircraft, part ship, literally travel on a cushion of air. This means that they can travel both over water and over land. Providing the surface is not too rough, very high speeds are possible over water.
Britain invented the air cushion vehicle and so far leads the world in their development.

SR-N1: Prototype Hovercraft.
Length: 30 ft.   Speed: 30 m.p.h.

SR-N2: First passenger-carrying Hovercraft.
Weight: 27 tons. Length: 65 ft. Speed: 87 m.p.h.

VICKERS VA-3: Air cushion vehicle.
Weight: 14 tons. Length: 55 ft. 7 in. Speed: 63 m.p.h.

TOP: SR-N4 Hovercraft *Princess Margaret*.
Weight: 160 tons.   Length: 128 ft. 6 in.   Speed: 90 m.p.h.
Carrying up to 228 passengers and 32 cars, this is
the world's biggest air cushion vehicle.

BOTTOM LEFT: SR-N5: Commercial Hovercraft.
Weight: 7 tons.   Length: 38 ft. 9 in.
Speed: 76 m.p.h.

BOTTOM RIGHT: SR-N6: Commercial Hovercraft.
Weight: 9 tons.   Length: 48 ft 5 in.
Speed: 70 m.p.h.

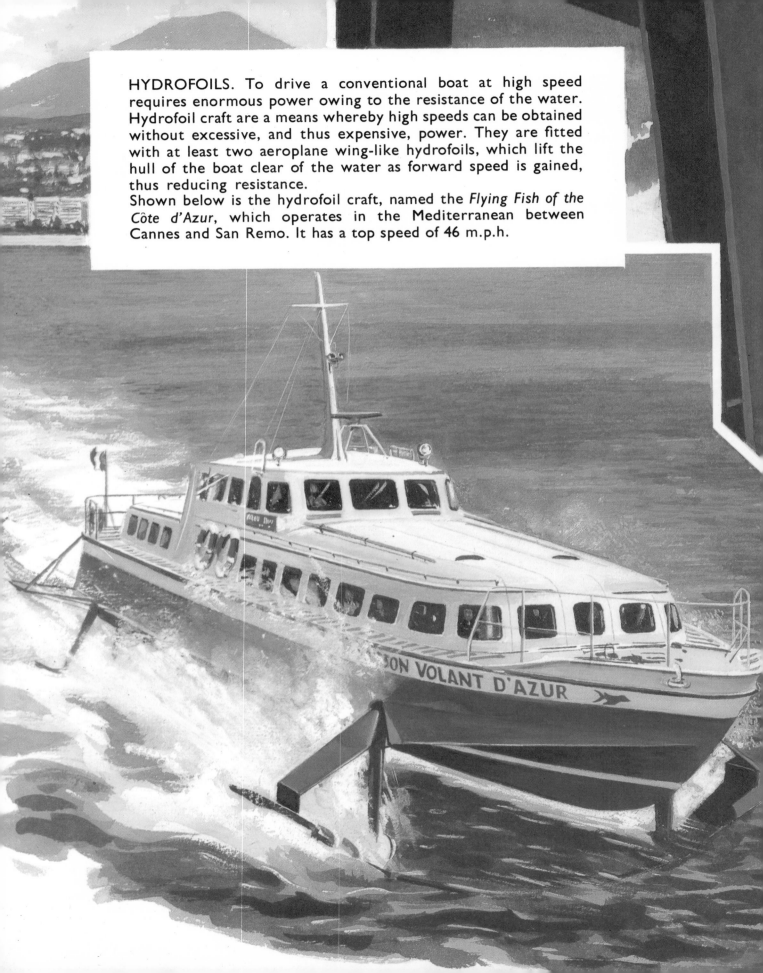

HYDROFOILS. To drive a conventional boat at high speed requires enormous power owing to the resistance of the water. Hydrofoil craft are a means whereby high speeds can be obtained without excessive, and thus expensive, power. They are fitted with at least two aeroplane wing-like hydrofoils, which lift the hull of the boat clear of the water as forward speed is gained, thus reducing resistance.

Shown below is the hydrofoil craft, named the *Flying Fish of the Côte d'Azur*, which operates in the Mediterranean between Cannes and San Remo. It has a top speed of 46 m.p.h.

MONORAILS. New conventional railways are expensive to build and occupy a great deal of valuable land. Monorails overcome some of these disadvantages. Relatively light, they use an overhead rail which can be led over buildings and other obstacles. The picture shows an experimental French monorail. Suspended by two bogies, it has a top speed of 60 m.p.h.

DROP FRAME LOW LOADER, used for transporting very heavy loads.

Transport is the lifeblood of a modern nation. Much of the freight involved, such as coal and other raw materials, and heavy machinery, is carried by the railway systems, but an increasing amount is carried by road. This is partly because it is often cheaper, and because almost always it is more convenient, as roads tend to go nearer to the destination of the goods than a railway.

This trend has been accelerated by the construction of the extensive Motorway systems in America and Europe, which permit heavy goods to be carried at high speed between industrial centres and ports with the minimum of interruptions. The motorways have, in turn, led to the development of special vehicles, a number of which are illustrated here.

HOVER TRANSPORTER.
Used for carrying transformers weighing up to 200 tons. The compressor vehicle at the rear forces air under the transporter. This reduces the load on the wheels and thus eases the burden on bridges.

TANKER.
Typical road fuel tanker.
Capacity: 6,000 gallons.

CAR TRANSPORTER.
Maximum capacity:
7 cars.
Can be converted into a single platform transporter.

CONTAINER ON SEMI-TRAILER.
Typical vehicle used for transporting standard 40-ft. containers.

PLATFORM SEMI-TRAILER.
Maximum load: 23 tons.
This is the commonest form of transporter used in Great Britain.

Many vehicles, for example those carrying raw materials such as coal or ore, are required to dump their load at their destination. To facilitate this, vehicles have been developed in which the body can be raised hydraulically so that the load slides off. The trucks normally tip the contents out at the back, but special vehicles are available which empty sideways. These are useful for widening roads or reinforcing embankments.

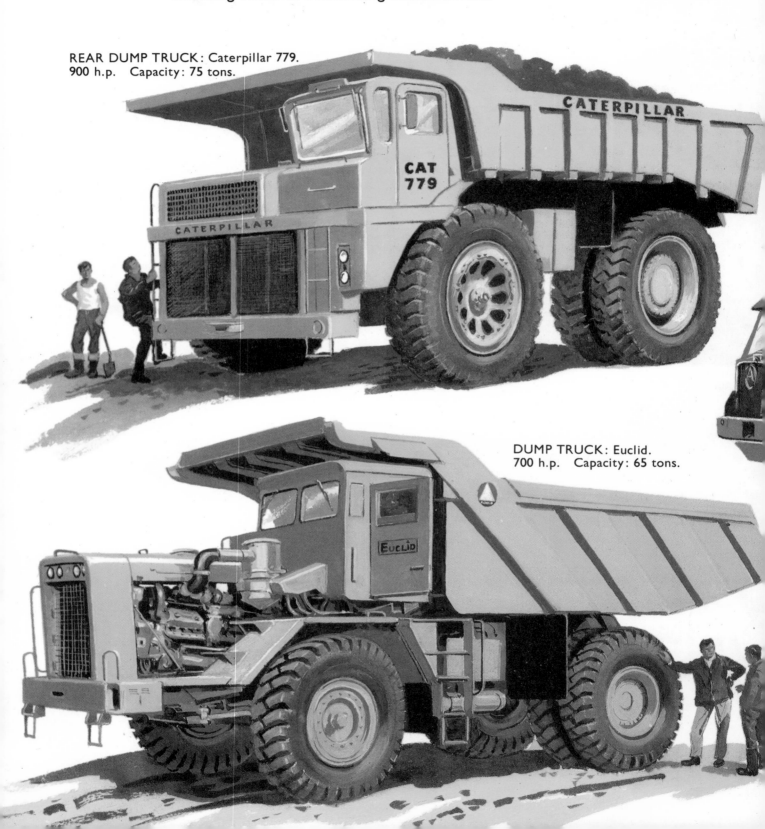

REAR DUMP TRUCK: Caterpillar 779.
900 h.p.   Capacity: 75 tons.

DUMP TRUCK: Euclid.
700 h.p.   Capacity: 65 tons.

SIDE-TIP TRUCK.

ARTICULATED TIPPER.

REAR DUMP TRUCK.
12 h.p. Capacity: 20 tons.

AIRCRAFT REFUELLER.
Typical of the special bowsers used for refuelling aircraft is this 12,000-gallon capacity Thompson 'Bristol'. It has been designed for refuelling the Concorde and other supersonic jets.

ARTICULATED TRANSPORTER.
For carrying cable drums. These are fitted with a winch for hauling the heavy drums into position.

THORNEYCROFT ANTAR TRACTOR.

ALVIS STALWART MUNITIONS TRUCK

Transport problems in the army have led to the development of a large number of special vehicles. Army equipment by its very nature tends to be heavy and cumbersome, and thus large vehicles are needed to move it. Heaviest items of all are the tanks. When travelling long distances, or when they have broken down, these are carried on special transporters. The transporters have winches for pulling the tank into position and multi-wheel units at each end to spread the load as much as possible. Army vehicles often have to travel over rough and muddy terrain, and usually have four-wheel drive for increased mobility. Tracked vehicles are used for moving heavy guns.

CENTURION ARK BRIDGE-LAYING TANK.

U.S. FLYING CRANE.

ROUGH TERRAIN CRANE.

FREIGHTLINER TRAIN. Special freight depots have been built to transfer large freight containers from road vehicles to trains, and from trains to vehicles. Big straddle cranes are used for loading and unloading.

DOCKS. A major development in sea freight has been the introduction of the standard freight containers and of the special container ships to carry them. There are many advantages. Instead of a very large number of relatively small items of cargo of varying size and shape, which have to be loaded into the holds individually, a smaller number of standard containers can be stacked one on top of the other.

To unload and load the containers huge transporter cranes are used similar to the one shown in the illustration. Below is a Henley fork-lift truck, the biggest in the world. This fork-lift truck can handle loads of up to 30 tons.

COAL MINING

Nowhere are machines put to better use than in mines. Until quite recently mining coal, in addition to being dangerous, was extremely hard work. Today it is less dangerous and machines do much of the work of cutting the coal and carrying it to the surface.

An early machine was the Meco-Moore Cutter-Loader which advanced along the coal face at the rate of two feet a minute. This was replaced by the Anderton Shearer Loader, one of the most popular and effective power loading machines ever introduced into British mines.